Next 90 Nation

War Map

WARNING:

By Using The Next 90 Nation War Map

You may change the course of your life:

PROCEED WITH EXTREME INTENTION

BODY

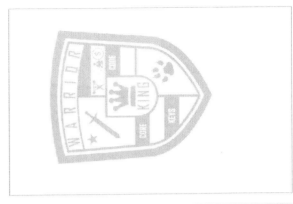

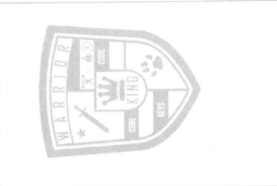

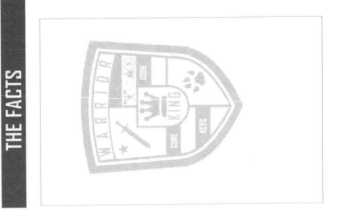

THE FACTS | THE GAP | 12 WEEKS | 12 MONTHS

BEING

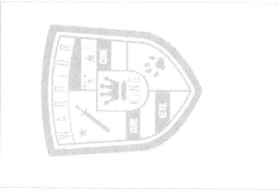

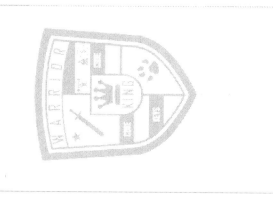

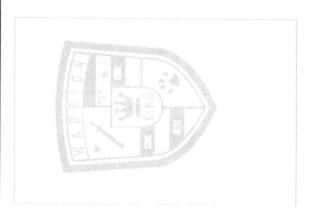

BALANCE

THE FACTS	THE GAP	12 WEEKS	12 MONTHS

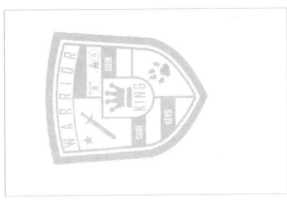

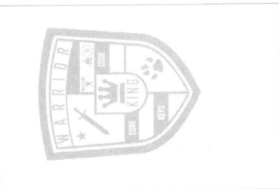

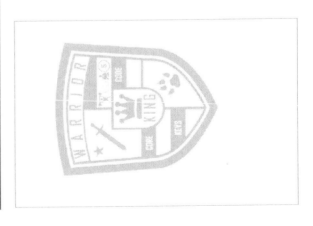

BUSINESS

THE FACTS	THE GAP	12 WEEKS	12 MONTHS

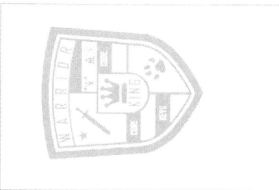

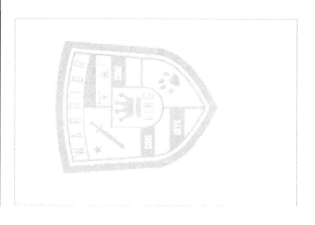

A New Week

New Targets

Body:
Being:
Balance:
Business:

The ONE THING This Week

Key 1	Key 2	Key 3	Key 4

Key Actions

Key 1

What	
Why	
When	
How	

Key 2

What	
Why	
When	
How	

Key 3

What	
Why	
When	
How	

Key 4

What	
Why	
When	
How	

Date: ___/___/___

Daily Game Points

Core 4 Before the Door

Body: Did I Sweat Today?   ☐ Yes   ☐ No

    Fitness   ☐ .5

    Fuel   ☐ .5

Being:

    Meditation   ☐ .5

    Memoirs   ☐ .5

Balance:

    Partner   ☐ .5

    Posterity   ☐ .5

Business:

    Discovery   ☐ .5

    Declare   ☐ .5

Total / 4pts   ☐

Power Zone   ☐ 4   ☐ 3   ☐ 2   ☐ 1   ☐ DNC

Did I Stack?   ☐ Yes 1pt   ☐ No 0pts

Total Score (Core 4 + Stack pts)   ☐

Power Zone Number   ☐

Insights From Meditation

Date: __/__/__

Daily Game Points

Core 4 Before the Door

Body: Did I Sweat Today? ☐ Yes ☐ No

Fitness ☐ .5

Fuel ☐ .5

Being:

Meditation ☐ .5

Memoirs ☐ .5

Balance:

Partner ☐ .5

Posterity ☐ .5

Business:

Discovery ☐ .5

Declare ☐ .5

Total / 4pts ☐

Power Zone ☐ 4 ☐ 3 ☐ 2 ☐ 1 ☐ DNC

Did I Stack? ☐ Yes 1pt ☐ No 0pts

Total Score (Core 4 + Stack pts) ☐

Power Zone Number ☐

Insights From Meditation

Date: ___/___/___

Daily Game Points

Core 4 Before the Door

Body: **Did I Sweat Today?** ☐ Yes ☐ No

    Fitness ☐ .5

    Fuel ☐ .5

Being:

    Meditation ☐ .5

    Memoirs ☐ .5

Balance:

    Partner ☐ .5

    Posterity ☐ .5

Business:

    Discovery ☐ .5

    Declare ☐ .5

Total / 4pts ☐

Power Zone ☐ 4 ☐ 3 ☐ 2 ☐ 1 ☐ DNC

Did I Stack? ☐ Yes 1pt ☐ No 0pts

Total Score (Core 4 + Stack pts) ☐

Power Zone Number ☐

Insights From Meditation

Date: ___/___/___

Daily Game Points

Core 4 Before the Door

Body: Did I Sweat Today?   ☐ Yes   ☐ No
- Fitness ☐ .5
- Fuel ☐ .5

Being:
- Meditation ☐ .5
- Memoirs ☐ .5

Balance:
- Partner ☐ .5
- Posterity ☐ .5

Business:
- Discovery ☐ .5
- Declare ☐ .5

Total / 4pts ☐

Power Zone ☐ 4   ☐ 3   ☐ 2   ☐ 1   ☐ DNC

Did I Stack? ☐ Yes 1pt   ☐ No 0pts

Total Score (Core 4 + Stack pts) ☐

Power Zone Number ☐

Insights From Meditation

Date: ___/___/___

Daily Game Points

Core 4 Before the Door

Body: Did I Sweat Today? ☐ Yes   ☐ No
  Fitness ☐ .5
  Fuel ☐ .5

Being:
  Meditation ☐ .5
  Memoirs ☐ .5

Balance:
  Partner ☐ .5
  Posterity ☐ .5

Business:
  Discovery ☐ .5
  Declare ☐ .5

Total / 4pts ☐

Power Zone ☐ 4 ☐ 3 ☐ 2 ☐ 1 ☐ DNC

Did I Stack? ☐ Yes 1pt ☐ No 0pts

Total Score (Core 4 + Stack pts) ☐

Power Zone Number ☐

Insights From Meditation

Date: __/__/__

Daily Game Points

Core 4 Before the Door

Body: Did I Sweat Today? ☐ Yes ☐ No

    Fitness ☐ .5

    Fuel ☐ .5

Being:

    Meditation ☐ .5

    Memoirs ☐ .5

Balance:

    Partner ☐ .5

    Posterity ☐ .5

Business:

    Discovery ☐ .5

    Declare ☐ .5

Total / 4pts ☐

Power Zone ☐ 4 ☐ 3 ☐ 2 ☐ 1 ☐ DNC

Did I Stack? ☐ Yes 1pt ☐ No 0pts

Total Score (Core 4 + Stack pts) ☐

Power Zone Number ☐

Insights From Meditation

Date: ___ / ___ / ___

Daily Game Points

Core 4 Before the Door

Body: Did I Sweat Today? ☐ Yes   ☐ No

    Fitness   ☐ .5

    Fuel   ☐ .5

Being:

    Meditation   ☐ .5

    Memoirs   ☐ .5

Balance:

    Partner   ☐ .5

    Posterity   ☐ .5

Business:

    Discovery   ☐ .5

    Declare   ☐ .5

Total / 4pts   ☐

Power Zone ☐ 4 ☐ 3 ☐ 2 ☐ 1 ☐ DNC

Did I Stack?   ☐ Yes 1pt   ☐ No 0pts

Total Score (Core 4 + Stack pts)   ☐

Power Zone Number   ☐

Insights From Meditation

The General's Tent
Review & Report

Core 4 Points out of 28 □

Stack Points out of 7 □

Did I Complete the ONE THING? Yes = 1pt □

Did I Complete THE 4 KEYS? 1 point each + □

Total out of 40 □

Lessons Learned Within:

Body:

Being:

Balance:

Business:

The Stack:

The One Thing:

The Four Keys:

The General's Tent

Course Corrections?

Body:

Being:

Balance:

Business:

The Stack:

The One Thing:

The Four Keys:

Congratulations
Time to Celebrate!

A New Week

New Targets

Body:
Being:
Balance:
Business:

The ONE THING This Week

Key 1	Key 2	Key 3	Key 4

Key Actions

Key 1

What	
Why	
When	
How	

Key 2

What	
Why	
When	
How	

Key 3

What	
Why	
When	
How	

Key 4

What	
Why	
When	
How	

Date: ___/___/___

Daily Game Points

Core 4 Before the Door

Body: **Did I Sweat Today?** ☐ Yes ☐ No

    Fitness ☐ .5

    Fuel ☐ .5

Being:

    Meditation ☐ .5

    Memoirs ☐ .5

Balance:

    Partner ☐ .5

    Posterity ☐ .5

Business:

    Discovery ☐ .5

    Declare ☐ .5

Total / 4pts ☐

Power Zone ☐ 4 ☐ 3 ☐ 2 ☐ 1 ☐ DNC

Did I Stack? ☐ Yes 1pt ☐ No 0pts

Total Score (Core 4 + Stack pts) ☐

Power Zone Number ☐

Insights From Meditation

Date: ___/___/___

Daily Game Points

Core 4 Before the Door

Body: Did I Sweat Today? ☐ Yes   ☐ No

   Fitness   ☐ .5

   Fuel   ☐ .5

Being:

   Meditation   ☐ .5

   Memoirs   ☐ .5

Balance:

   Partner   ☐ .5

   Posterity   ☐ .5

Business:

   Discovery   ☐ .5

   Declare   ☐ .5

Total / 4pts   ☐

Power Zone   ☐ 4   ☐ 3   ☐ 2   ☐ 1   ☐ DNC

Did I Stack?   ☐ Yes 1pt   ☐ No 0pts

Total Score (Core 4 + Stack pts)   ☐

Power Zone Number   ☐

Insights From Meditation

Date: ___ / ___ / ___

Daily Game Points

Core 4 Before the Door

Body: **Did I Sweat Today?** ☐ Yes   ☐ No
    Fitness ☐ .5
    Fuel ☐ .5

Being:
    Meditation ☐ .5
    Memoirs ☐ .5

Balance:
    Partner ☐ .5
    Posterity ☐ .5

Business:
    Discovery ☐ .5
    Declare ☐ .5

Total / 4pts ☐

Power Zone ☐ 4   ☐ 3   ☐ 2   ☐ 1   ☐ DNC

Did I Stack? ☐ Yes 1pt   ☐ No 0pts

Total Score (Core 4 + Stack pts) ☐

Power Zone Number ☐

Insights From Meditation

Date: ___ / ___ / ___

Daily Game Points

Core 4 Before the Door

Body: Did I Sweat Today? ☐ Yes ☐ No

    Fitness ☐ .5

    Fuel ☐ .5

Being:

    Meditation ☐ .5

    Memoirs ☐ .5

Balance:

    Partner ☐ .5

    Posterity ☐ .5

Business:

    Discovery ☐ .5

    Declare ☐ .5

Total / 4pts ☐

Power Zone ☐ 4 ☐ 3 ☐ 2 ☐ 1 ☐ DNC

Did I Stack? ☐ Yes 1pt ☐ No 0pts

Total Score (Core 4 + Stack pts) ☐

Power Zone Number ☐

Insights From Meditation

Date: ___/___/___

Daily Game Points

Core 4 Before the Door

Body: Did I Sweat Today? ☐ Yes   ☐ No
- Fitness ☐ .5
- Fuel ☐ .5

Being:
- Meditation ☐ .5
- Memoirs ☐ .5

Balance:
- Partner ☐ .5
- Posterity ☐ .5

Business:
- Discovery ☐ .5
- Declare ☐ .5

Total / 4pts ☐

Power Zone ☐ 4 ☐ 3 ☐ 2 ☐ 1 ☐ DNC

Did I Stack? ☐ Yes 1pt   ☐ No 0pts

Total Score (Core 4 + Stack pts) ☐

Power Zone Number ☐

Insights From Meditation

Date: ___/___/___

Daily Game Points

Core 4 Before the Door

Body: **Did I Sweat Today?** ☐ Yes ☐ No

  Fitness ☐ .5

  Fuel ☐ .5

Being:

  Meditation ☐ .5

  Memoirs ☐ .5

Balance:

  Partner ☐ .5

  Posterity ☐ .5

Business:

  Discovery ☐ .5

  Declare ☐ .5

Total / 4pts ☐

Power Zone ☐ 4 ☐ 3 ☐ 2 ☐ 1 ☐ DNC

Did I Stack? ☐ Yes 1pt ☐ No 0pts

Total Score (Core 4 + Stack pts) ☐

Power Zone Number ☐

Insights From Meditation

Date: ___/___/___

Daily Game Points

Core 4 Before the Door

Body: Did I Sweat Today? ☐ Yes   ☐ No
- Fitness   ☐ .5
- Fuel   ☐ .5

Being:
- Meditation   ☐ .5
- Memoirs   ☐ .5

Balance:
- Partner   ☐ .5
- Posterity   ☐ .5

Business:
- Discovery   ☐ .5
- Declare   ☐ .5

Total / 4pts   ☐

Power Zone ☐ 4   ☐ 3   ☐ 2   ☐ 1   ☐ DNC

Did I Stack?   ☐ Yes 1pt   ☐ No 0pts

Total Score (Core 4 + Stack pts)   ☐

Power Zone Number   ☐

Insights From Meditation

The General's Tent
Review & Report

Core 4 Points out of 28

Stack Points out of 7

Did I Complete the ONE THING? Yes = 1pt

Did I Complete THE 4 KEYS? 1 point each

☐
☐
☐
+ ☐
___
Total out of 40   ☐

Lessons Learned Within:

Body:

Being:

Balance:

Business:

The Stack:

The One Thing:

The Four Keys:

The General's Tent

Course Corrections?

Body:

Being:

Balance:

Business:

The Stack:

The One Thing:

The Four Keys:

Congratulations

Time to Celebrate!

A New Week

New Targets

Body:

Being:

Balance:

Business:

The ONE THING This Week

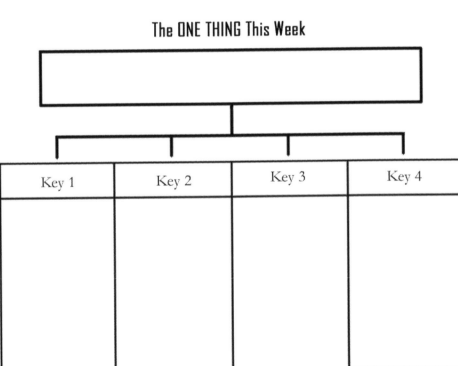

Key 1	Key 2	Key 3	Key 4

Key Actions

Key 1

What	
Why	
When	
How	

Key 2

What	
Why	
When	
How	

Key 3

What	
Why	
When	
How	

Key 4

What	
Why	
When	
How	

Date: ___/___/___

Daily Game Points

Core 4 Before the Door

Body: **Did I Sweat Today?** ☐ Yes ☐ No

    Fitness ☐ .5

    Fuel ☐ .5

Being:

    Meditation ☐ .5

    Memoirs ☐ .5

Balance:

    Partner ☐ .5

    Posterity ☐ .5

Business:

    Discovery ☐ .5

    Declare ☐ .5

Total / 4pts ☐

Power Zone ☐ 4 ☐ 3 ☐ 2 ☐ 1 ☐ DNC

Did I Stack? ☐ Yes 1pt ☐ No 0pts

Total Score (Core 4 + Stack pts) ☐

Power Zone Number ☐

Insights From Meditation

Date: __ / __ / __

Daily Game Points

Core 4 Before the Door

Body: Did I Sweat Today? ☐ Yes   ☐ No

    Fitness ☐ .5

    Fuel ☐ .5

Being:

    Meditation ☐ .5

    Memoirs ☐ .5

Balance:

    Partner ☐ .5

    Posterity ☐ .5

Business:

    Discovery ☐ .5

    Declare ☐ .5

Total / 4pts ☐

Power Zone ☐ 4   ☐ 3   ☐ 2   ☐ 1   ☐ DNC

Did I Stack? ☐ Yes 1pt   ☐ No 0pts

Total Score (Core 4 + Stack pts) ☐

Power Zone Number ☐

Insights From Meditation

Date: ___/___/___

Daily Game Points

Core 4 Before the Door

Body: Did I Sweat Today? ☐ Yes   ☐ No

    Fitness ☐ .5

    Fuel ☐ .5

Being:

    Meditation ☐ .5

    Memoirs ☐ .5

Balance:

    Partner ☐ .5

    Posterity ☐ .5

Business:

    Discovery ☐ .5

    Declare ☐ .5

Total / 4pts ☐

Power Zone ☐ 4 ☐ 3 ☐ 2 ☐ 1 ☐ DNC

Did I Stack? ☐ Yes 1pt   ☐ No 0pts

Total Score (Core 4 + Stack pts) ☐

Power Zone Number ☐

Insights From Meditation

Date: ___ / ___ / ___

Daily Game Points

Core 4 Before the Door

Body: **Did I Sweat Today?** ☐ Yes ☐ No

    Fitness   ☐ .5

    Fuel   ☐ .5

Being:

    Meditation   ☐ .5

    Memoirs   ☐ .5

Balance:

    Partner   ☐ .5

    Posterity   ☐ .5

Business:

    Discovery   ☐ .5

    Declare   ☐ .5

Total / 4pts ☐

Power Zone ☐ 4 ☐ 3 ☐ 2 ☐ 1 ☐ DNC

Did I Stack? ☐ Yes 1pt ☐ No 0pts

Total Score (Core 4 + Stack pts) ☐

Power Zone Number ☐

Insights From Meditation

Date: ___/___/___

Daily Game Points

Core 4 Before the Door

Body: Did I Sweat Today? ☐ Yes   ☐ No

    Fitness ☐ .5

    Fuel ☐ .5

Being:

    Meditation ☐ .5

    Memoirs ☐ .5

Balance:

    Partner ☐ .5

    Posterity ☐ .5

Business:

    Discovery ☐ .5

    Declare ☐ .5

Total / 4pts ☐

Power Zone ☐ 4   ☐ 3   ☐ 2   ☐ 1   ☐ DNC

Did I Stack? ☐ Yes 1pt   ☐ No 0pts

Total Score (Core 4 + Stack pts) ☐

Power Zone Number ☐

Insights From Meditation

Date: __ / __ / __

Daily Game Points

Core 4 Before the Door

Body: **Did I Sweat Today?**   ☐ Yes   ☐ No

    Fitness   ☐ .5

    Fuel   ☐ .5

Being:

    Meditation   ☐ .5

    Memoirs   ☐ .5

Balance:

    Partner   ☐ .5

    Posterity   ☐ .5

Business:

    Discovery   ☐ .5

    Declare   ☐ .5

Total / 4pts   ☐

Power Zone   ☐ 4   ☐ 3   ☐ 2   ☐ 1   ☐ DNC

Did I Stack?   ☐ Yes 1pt   ☐ No 0pts

Total Score (Core 4 + Stack pts)   ☐

Power Zone Number   ☐

Insights From Meditation

Date: ___/___/___

Daily Game Points

Core 4 Before the Door

Body: Did I Sweat Today? ☐ Yes   ☐ No

    Fitness ☐ .5

    Fuel ☐ .5

Being:

    Meditation ☐ .5

    Memoirs ☐ .5

Balance:

    Partner ☐ .5

    Posterity ☐ .5

Business:

    Discovery ☐ .5

    Declare ☐ .5

Total / 4pts ☐

Power Zone ☐ 4   ☐ 3   ☐ 2   ☐ 1   ☐ DNC

Did I Stack? ☐ Yes 1pt   ☐ No 0pts

Total Score (Core 4 + Stack pts) ☐

Power Zone Number ☐

Insights From Meditation

The General's Tent
Review & Report

Core 4 Points out of 28

Stack Points out of 7

Did I Complete the ONE THING? Yes = 1pt

Did I Complete THE 4 KEYS? 1 point each

☐
☐
☐
+ ☐
___
Total out of 40 ☐

Lessons Learned Within:

Body:

Being:

Balance:

Business:

The Stack:

The One Thing:

The Four Keys:

The General's Tent

Course Corrections?

Body:

Being:

Balance:

Business:

The Stack:

The One Thing:

The Four Keys:

Congratulations

Time to Celebrate!

A New Week

New Targets

Body:	
Being:	
Balance:	
Business:	

The ONE THING This Week

Key 1	Key 2	Key 3	Key 4

Key Actions

Key 1

What	
Why	
When	
How	

Key 2

What	
Why	
When	
How	

Key 3

What	
Why	
When	
How	

Key 4

What	
Why	
When	
How	

Date: ___/___/___

Daily Game Points

Core 4 Before the Door

Body: Did I Sweat Today? ☐ Yes ☐ No

    Fitness ☐ .5

    Fuel ☐ .5

Being:

    Meditation ☐ .5

    Memoirs ☐ .5

Balance:

    Partner ☐ .5

    Posterity ☐ .5

Business:

    Discovery ☐ .5

    Declare ☐ .5

Total / 4pts ☐

Power Zone ☐ 4 ☐ 3 ☐ 2 ☐ 1 ☐ DNC

Did I Stack? ☐ Yes 1pt ☐ No 0pts

Total Score (Core 4 + Stack pts) ☐

Power Zone Number ☐

Insights From Meditation

Date: ___ / ___ / ___

Daily Game Points

Core 4 Before the Door

Body: Did I Sweat Today?   ☐ Yes   ☐ No

    Fitness   ☐ .5

    Fuel   ☐ .5

Being:

    Meditation   ☐ .5

    Memoirs   ☐ .5

Balance:

    Partner   ☐ .5

    Posterity   ☐ .5

Business:

    Discovery   ☐ .5

    Declare   ☐ .5

Total / 4pts   ☐

Power Zone   ☐ 4   ☐ 3   ☐ 2   ☐ 1   ☐ DNC

Did I Stack?   ☐ Yes 1pt   ☐ No 0pts

Total Score (Core 4 + Stack pts)   ☐

Power Zone Number   ☐

Insights From Meditation

Date: ___/___/___

Daily Game Points

Core 4 Before the Door

Body: Did I Sweat Today? ☐ Yes ☐ No

    Fitness ☐ .5

    Fuel ☐ .5

Being:

    Meditation ☐ .5

    Memoirs ☐ .5

Balance:

    Partner ☐ .5

    Posterity ☐ .5

Business:

    Discovery ☐ .5

    Declare ☐ .5

Total / 4pts ☐

Power Zone ☐ 4 ☐ 3 ☐ 2 ☐ 1 ☐ DNC

Did I Stack? ☐ Yes 1pt ☐ No 0pts

Total Score (Core 4 + Stack pts) ☐

Power Zone Number ☐

Insights From Meditation

Date: ___/___/___

Daily Game Points

Core 4 Before the Door

Body: Did I Sweat Today? ☐ Yes   ☐ No

    Fitness ☐ .5

    Fuel ☐ .5

Being:

    Meditation ☐ .5

    Memoirs ☐ .5

Balance:

    Partner ☐ .5

    Posterity ☐ .5

Business:

    Discovery ☐ .5

    Declare ☐ .5

Total / 4pts ☐

Power Zone ☐ 4 ☐ 3 ☐ 2 ☐ 1 ☐ DNC

Did I Stack? ☐ Yes 1pt   ☐ No 0pts

Total Score (Core 4 + Stack pts) ☐

Power Zone Number ☐

Insights From Meditation

Date: ___/___/___

Daily Game Points

Core 4 Before the Door

Body: **Did I Sweat Today?** ☐ Yes   ☐ No

    Fitness ☐ .5

    Fuel ☐ .5

Being:

    Meditation ☐ .5

    Memoirs ☐ .5

Balance:

    Partner ☐ .5

    Posterity ☐ .5

Business:

    Discovery ☐ .5

    Declare ☐ .5

Total / 4pts ☐

Power Zone ☐ 4 ☐ 3 ☐ 2 ☐ 1 ☐ DNC

Did I Stack? ☐ Yes 1pt   ☐ No 0pts

Total Score (Core 4 + Stack pts) ☐

Power Zone Number ☐

Insights From Meditation

Date: ___/___/___

Daily Game Points

Core 4 Before the Door

Body: Did I Sweat Today? ☐ Yes   ☐ No

    Fitness ☐ .5

    Fuel ☐ .5

Being:

    Meditation ☐ .5

    Memoirs ☐ .5

Balance:

    Partner ☐ .5

    Posterity ☐ .5

Business:

    Discovery ☐ .5

    Declare ☐ .5

Total / 4pts ☐

Power Zone ☐ 4 ☐ 3 ☐ 2 ☐ 1 ☐ DNC

Did I Stack? ☐ Yes 1pt   ☐ No 0pts

Total Score (Core 4 + Stack pts) ☐

Power Zone Number ☐

Insights From Meditation

Date: ___/___/___

Daily Game Points

Core 4 Before the Door

Body: Did I Sweat Today?   ☐ Yes   ☐ No
    Fitness   ☐ .5
    Fuel   ☐ .5

Being:
    Meditation   ☐ .5
    Memoirs   ☐ .5

Balance:
    Partner   ☐ .5
    Posterity   ☐ .5

Business:
    Discovery   ☐ .5
    Declare   ☐ .5

Total / 4pts   ☐

Power Zone   ☐ 4   ☐ 3   ☐ 2   ☐ 1   ☐ DNC

Did I Stack?   ☐ Yes 1pt   ☐ No 0pts

Total Score (Core 4 + Stack pts)   ☐

Power Zone Number   ☐

Insights From Meditation

The General's Tent
Review & Report

Core 4 Points out of 28 ☐

Stack Points out of 7 ☐

Did I Complete the ONE THING? Yes = 1pt ☐

Did I Complete THE 4 KEYS? 1 point each **+** ☐

Total out of 40 ☐

Lessons Learned Within:

Body:

Being:

Balance:

Business:

The Stack:

The One Thing:

The Four Keys:

The General's Tent

Course Corrections?

Body:
Being:
Balance:
Business:
The Stack:
The One Thing:
The Four Keys:

Congratulations
Time to Celebrate!

30 Day Benchmark

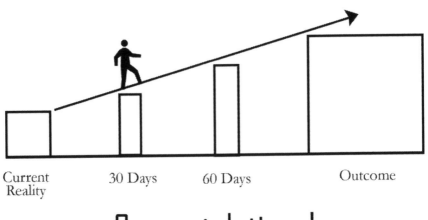

Current
Reality   30 Days   60 Days   Outcome

Congratulations!

Where am I falling off?

Did I make the Outcome too small?

Benchmark Insights

A New Week

New Targets

Body:

Being:

Balance:

Business:

The ONE THING This Week

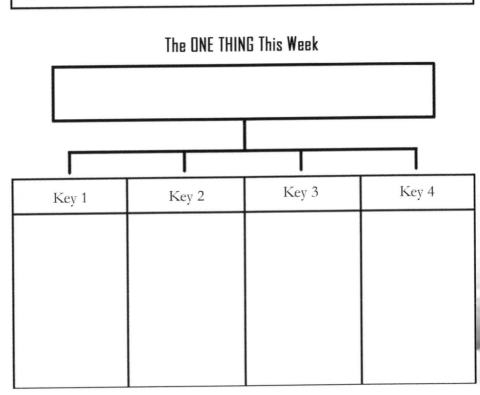

Key 1	Key 2	Key 3	Key 4

Key Actions

Key 1

What	
Why	
When	
How	

Key 2

What	
Why	
When	
How	

Key 3

What	
Why	
When	
How	

Key 4

What	
Why	
When	
How	

Date: ___/___/___

Daily Game Points

Core 4 Before the Door

Body: Did I Sweat Today? ☐ Yes ☐ No

   Fitness ☐ .5

   Fuel ☐ .5

Being:

   Meditation ☐ .5

   Memoirs ☐ .5

Balance:

   Partner ☐ .5

   Posterity ☐ .5

Business:

   Discovery ☐ .5

   Declare ☐ .5

Total / 4pts ☐

Power Zone ☐ 4 ☐ 3 ☐ 2 ☐ 1 ☐ DNC

Did I Stack? ☐ Yes 1pt ☐ No 0pts

Total Score (Core 4 + Stack pts) ☐

Power Zone Number ☐

Insights From Meditation

Date: __ / __ / __

Daily Game Points

Core 4 Before the Door

Body: Did I Sweat Today? ☐ Yes   ☐ No

    Fitness   ☐ .5

    Fuel   ☐ .5

Being:

    Meditation   ☐ .5

    Memoirs   ☐ .5

Balance:

    Partner   ☐ .5

    Posterity   ☐ .5

Business:

    Discovery   ☐ .5

    Declare   ☐ .5

Total / 4pts   ☐

Power Zone ☐ 4   ☐ 3   ☐ 2   ☐ 1   ☐ DNC

Did I Stack?   ☐ Yes 1pt   ☐ No 0pts

Total Score (Core 4 + Stack pts)   ☐

Power Zone Number   ☐

Insights From Meditation

Date: ___/___/___

Daily Game Points

Core 4 Before the Door

Body: Did I Sweat Today?   ☐ Yes   ☐ No
    Fitness   ☐ .5
    Fuel   ☐ .5

Being:
    Meditation   ☐ .5
    Memoirs   ☐ .5

Balance:
    Partner   ☐ .5
    Posterity   ☐ .5

Business:
    Discovery   ☐ .5
    Declare   ☐ .5

Total / 4pts   ☐

Power Zone   ☐ 4   ☐ 3   ☐ 2   ☐ 1   ☐ DNC

Did I Stack?   ☐ Yes 1pt   ☐ No 0pts

Total Score (Core 4 + Stack pts)   ☐

Power Zone Number   ☐

Insights From Meditation

Date: __/__/__

Daily Game Points

Core 4 Before the Door

Body: **Did I Sweat Today?** ☐ Yes   ☐ No

    Fitness ☐ .5

    Fuel ☐ .5

Being:

    Meditation ☐ .5

    Memoirs ☐ .5

Balance:

    Partner ☐ .5

    Posterity ☐ .5

Business:

    Discovery ☐ .5

    Declare ☐ .5

Total / 4pts ☐

Power Zone ☐ 4   ☐ 3   ☐ 2   ☐ 1   ☐ DNC

Did I Stack? ☐ Yes 1pt   ☐ No 0pts

Total Score (Core 4 + Stack pts) ☐

Power Zone Number ☐

Insights From Meditation

Date: ___/___/___

Daily Game Points

Core 4 Before the Door

Body: Did I Sweat Today? ☐ Yes ☐ No

    Fitness ☐ .5

    Fuel ☐ .5

Being:

    Meditation ☐ .5

    Memoirs ☐ .5

Balance:

    Partner ☐ .5

    Posterity ☐ .5

Business:

    Discovery ☐ .5

    Declare ☐ .5

Total / 4pts ☐

Power Zone ☐ 4 ☐ 3 ☐ 2 ☐ 1 ☐ DNC

Did I Stack? ☐ Yes 1pt ☐ No 0pts

Total Score (Core 4 + Stack pts) ☐

Power Zone Number ☐

Insights From Meditation

Date: ___/___/___

Daily Game Points

Core 4 Before the Door

Body: **Did I Sweat Today?** ☐ Yes ☐ No

    Fitness   ☐ .5

    Fuel   ☐ .5

Being:

    Meditation   ☐ .5

    Memoirs   ☐ .5

Balance:

    Partner   ☐ .5

    Posterity   ☐ .5

Business:

    Discovery   ☐ .5

    Declare   ☐ .5

Total / 4pts   ☐

Power Zone   ☐ 4   ☐ 3   ☐ 2   ☐ 1   ☐ DNC

Did I Stack?   ☐ Yes 1pt   ☐ No 0pts

Total Score (Core 4 + Stack pts)   ☐

Power Zone Number   ☐

Insights From Meditation

Date: ___/___/___

Daily Game Points

Core 4 Before the Door

Body: Did I Sweat Today? ☐ Yes ☐ No
- Fitness ☐ .5
- Fuel ☐ .5

Being:
- Meditation ☐ .5
- Memoirs ☐ .5

Balance:
- Partner ☐ .5
- Posterity ☐ .5

Business:
- Discovery ☐ .5
- Declare ☐ .5

Total / 4pts ☐

Power Zone ☐ 4 ☐ 3 ☐ 2 ☐ 1 ☐ DNC

Did I Stack? ☐ Yes 1pt ☐ No 0pts

Total Score (Core 4 + Stack pts) ☐

Power Zone Number ☐

Insights From Meditation

The General's Tent
Review & Report

Core 4 Points out of 28 □

Stack Points out of 7 □

Did I Complete the ONE THING? Yes = 1pt □

Did I Complete THE 4 KEYS? 1 point each + □

Total out of 40 □

Lessons Learned Within:

Body:

Being:

Balance:

Business:

The Stack:

The One Thing:

The Four Keys:

The General's Tent

Course Corrections?

Body:

Being:

Balance:

Business:

The Stack:

The One Thing:

The Four Keys:

Congratulations

Time to Celebrate!

A New Week

New Targets

Body:
Being:
Balance:
Business:

The ONE THING This Week

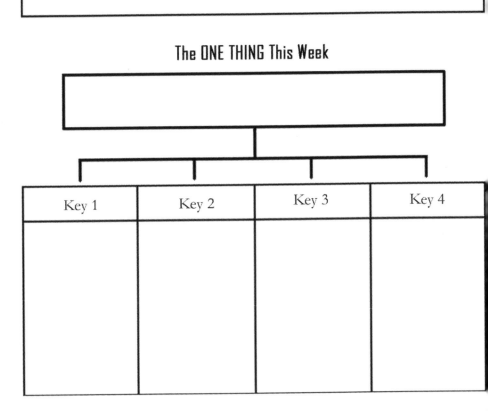

Key 1	Key 2	Key 3	Key 4

Key Actions

Key 1

What	
Why	
When	
How	

Key 2

What	
Why	
When	
How	

Key 3

What	
Why	
When	
How	

Key 4

What	
Why	
When	
How	

Date: ___/___/___

Daily Game Points

Core 4 Before the Door

Body: Did I Sweat Today? ☐ Yes ☐ No

    Fitness ☐ .5

    Fuel ☐ .5

Being:

    Meditation ☐ .5

    Memoirs ☐ .5

Balance:

    Partner ☐ .5

    Posterity ☐ .5

Business:

    Discovery ☐ .5

    Declare ☐ .5

Total / 4pts ☐

Power Zone ☐ 4 ☐ 3 ☐ 2 ☐ 1 ☐ DNC

Did I Stack? ☐ Yes 1pt ☐ No 0pts

Total Score (Core 4 + Stack pts) ☐

Power Zone Number ☐

Insights From Meditation

Date: ___/___/___

Daily Game Points

Core 4 Before the Door

Body: Did I Sweat Today? ☐ Yes ☐ No

Fitness ☐ .5

Fuel ☐ .5

Being:

Meditation ☐ .5

Memoirs ☐ .5

Balance:

Partner ☐ .5

Posterity ☐ .5

Business:

Discovery ☐ .5

Declare ☐ .5

Total / 4pts ☐

Power Zone ☐ 4 ☐ 3 ☐ 2 ☐ 1 ☐ DNC

Did I Stack? ☐ Yes 1pt ☐ No 0pts

Total Score (Core 4 + Stack pts) ☐

Power Zone Number ☐

Insights From Meditation

Date: ___/___/___

Daily Game Points

Core 4 Before the Door

Body: Did I Sweat Today? ☐ Yes   ☐ No

    Fitness   ☐ .5

    Fuel   ☐ .5

Being:

    Meditation   ☐ .5

    Memoirs   ☐ .5

Balance:

    Partner   ☐ .5

    Posterity   ☐ .5

Business:

    Discovery   ☐ .5

    Declare   ☐ .5

Total / 4pts   ☐

Power Zone   ☐ 4   ☐ 3   ☐ 2   ☐ 1   ☐ DNC

Did I Stack?   ☐ Yes 1pt   ☐ No 0pts

Total Score (Core 4 + Stack pts)   ☐

Power Zone Number   ☐

Insights From Meditation

Date: ___/___/___

Daily Game Points

Core 4 Before the Door

Body: Did I Sweat Today?   ☐ Yes   ☐ No

    Fitness   ☐ .5

    Fuel   ☐ .5

Being:

    Meditation   ☐ .5

    Memoirs   ☐ .5

Balance:

    Partner   ☐ .5

    Posterity   ☐ .5

Business:

    Discovery   ☐ .5

    Declare   ☐ .5

Total / 4pts   ☐

Power Zone   ☐ 4   ☐ 3   ☐ 2   ☐ 1   ☐ DNC

Did I Stack?   ☐ Yes 1pt   ☐ No 0pts

Total Score (Core 4 + Stack pts)   ☐

Power Zone Number   ☐

Insights From Meditation

Date: ___/___/___

Daily Game Points

Core 4 Before the Door

Body: Did I Sweat Today? ☐ Yes ☐ No

Fitness ☐ .5

Fuel ☐ .5

Being:

Meditation ☐ .5

Memoirs ☐ .5

Balance:

Partner ☐ .5

Posterity ☐ .5

Business:

Discovery ☐ .5

Declare ☐ .5

Total / 4pts ☐

Power Zone ☐ 4 ☐ 3 ☐ 2 ☐ 1 ☐ DNC

Did I Stack? ☐ Yes 1pt ☐ No 0pts

Total Score (Core 4 + Stack pts) ☐

Power Zone Number ☐

Insights From Meditation

Date: ___/___/___

Daily Game Points

Core 4 Before the Door

Body: Did I Sweat Today? ☐ Yes ☐ No

    Fitness ☐ .5

    Fuel ☐ .5

Being:

    Meditation ☐ .5

    Memoirs ☐ .5

Balance:

    Partner ☐ .5

    Posterity ☐ .5

Business:

    Discovery ☐ .5

    Declare ☐ .5

Total / 4pts ☐

Power Zone ☐ 4 ☐ 3 ☐ 2 ☐ 1 ☐ DNC

Did I Stack? ☐ Yes 1pt ☐ No 0pts

Total Score (Core 4 + Stack pts) ☐

Power Zone Number ☐

Insights From Meditation

Date: ___/___/___

Daily Game Points

Core 4 Before the Door

Body: Did I Sweat Today? ☐ Yes ☐ No

    Fitness ☐ .5

    Fuel ☐ .5

Being:

    Meditation ☐ .5

    Memoirs ☐ .5

Balance:

    Partner ☐ .5

    Posterity ☐ .5

Business:

    Discovery ☐ .5

    Declare ☐ .5

Total / 4pts ☐

Power Zone ☐ 4 ☐ 3 ☐ 2 ☐ 1 ☐ DNC

Did I Stack? ☐ Yes 1pt ☐ No 0pts

Total Score (Core 4 + Stack pts) ☐

Power Zone Number ☐

Insights From Meditation

The General's Tent
Review & Report

Core 4 Points out of 28 ☐

Stack Points out of 7 ☐

Did I Complete the ONE THING? Yes = 1pt ☐

Did I Complete THE 4 KEYS? 1 point each + ☐

Total out of 40 ☐

Lessons Learned Within:

Body:

Being:

Balance:

Business:

The Stack:

The One Thing:

The Four Keys:

The General's Tent

Course Corrections?

Body:

Being:

Balance:

Business:

The Stack:

The One Thing:

The Four Keys:

Congratulations
Time to Celebrate!

A New Week

New Targets

Body:
Being:
Balance:
Business:

The ONE THING This Week

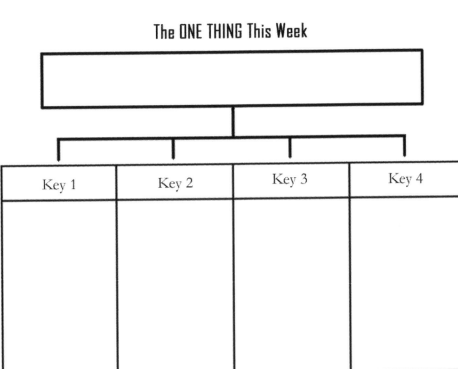

Key 1	Key 2	Key 3	Key 4

Key Actions

Key 1

What	
Why	
When	
How	

Key 2

What	
Why	
When	
How	

Key 3

What	
Why	
When	
How	

Key 4

What	
Why	
When	
How	

Date: ___/___/___

Daily Game Points

Core 4 Before the Door

Body: **Did I Sweat Today?** ☐ Yes   ☐ No
- Fitness   ☐ .5
- Fuel   ☐ .5

Being:
- Meditation   ☐ .5
- Memoirs   ☐ .5

Balance:
- Partner   ☐ .5
- Posterity   ☐ .5

Business:
- Discovery   ☐ .5
- Declare   ☐ .5

Total / 4pts   ☐

Power Zone ☐ 4 ☐ 3 ☐ 2 ☐ 1 ☐ DNC

Did I Stack?   ☐ Yes 1pt   ☐ No 0pts

Total Score (Core 4 + Stack pts)   ☐

Power Zone Number   ☐

Insights From Meditation

Date: ___/___/___

Daily Game Points

Core 4 Before the Door

Body: Did I Sweat Today? ☐ Yes ☐ No

    Fitness ☐ .5

    Fuel ☐ .5

Being:

    Meditation ☐ .5

    Memoirs ☐ .5

Balance:

    Partner ☐ .5

    Posterity ☐ .5

Business:

    Discovery ☐ .5

    Declare ☐ .5

Total / 4pts ☐

Power Zone ☐ 4 ☐ 3 ☐ 2 ☐ 1 ☐ DNC

Did I Stack? ☐ Yes 1pt ☐ No 0pts

Total Score (Core 4 + Stack pts) ☐

Power Zone Number ☐

Insights From Meditation

Date: ___/___/___

Daily Game Points

Core 4 Before the Door

Body: **Did I Sweat Today?** ☐ Yes ☐ No

    Fitness ☐ .5

    Fuel ☐ .5

Being:

    Meditation ☐ .5

    Memoirs ☐ .5

Balance:

    Partner ☐ .5

    Posterity ☐ .5

Business:

    Discovery ☐ .5

    Declare ☐ .5

Total / 4pts ☐

Power Zone ☐ 4 ☐ 3 ☐ 2 ☐ 1 ☐ DNC

Did I Stack? ☐ Yes 1pt ☐ No 0pts

Total Score (Core 4 + Stack pts) ☐

Power Zone Number ☐

Insights From Meditation

Date: ___/___/___

Daily Game Points

Core 4 Before the Door

Body: Did I Sweat Today? ☐ Yes ☐ No

    Fitness ☐ .5

    Fuel ☐ .5

Being:

    Meditation ☐ .5

    Memoirs ☐ .5

Balance:

    Partner ☐ .5

    Posterity ☐ .5

Business:

    Discovery ☐ .5

    Declare ☐ .5

Total / 4pts ☐

Power Zone ☐ 4 ☐ 3 ☐ 2 ☐ 1 ☐ DNC

Did I Stack? ☐ Yes 1pt ☐ No 0pts

Total Score (Core 4 + Stack pts) ☐

Power Zone Number ☐

Insights From Meditation

Date: __ / __ / __

Daily Game Points

Core 4 Before the Door

Body: **Did I Sweat Today?** ☐ Yes   ☐ No

    Fitness ☐ .5

    Fuel ☐ .5

Being:

    Meditation ☐ .5

    Memoirs ☐ .5

Balance:

    Partner ☐ .5

    Posterity ☐ .5

Business:

    Discovery ☐ .5

    Declare ☐ .5

Total / 4pts ☐

Power Zone ☐ 4   ☐ 3   ☐ 2   ☐ 1   ☐ DNC

Did I Stack? ☐ Yes 1pt   ☐ No 0pts

Total Score (Core 4 + Stack pts) ☐

Power Zone Number ☐

Insights From Meditation

Date: ___/___/___

Daily Game Points

Core 4 Before the Door

Body: Did I Sweat Today? ☐ Yes ☐ No

    Fitness ☐ .5

    Fuel ☐ .5

Being:

    Meditation ☐ .5

    Memoirs ☐ .5

Balance:

    Partner ☐ .5

    Posterity ☐ .5

Business:

    Discovery ☐ .5

    Declare ☐ .5

Total / 4pts ☐

Power Zone ☐ 4 ☐ 3 ☐ 2 ☐ 1 ☐ DNC

Did I Stack? ☐ Yes 1pt ☐ No 0pts

Total Score (Core 4 + Stack pts) ☐

Power Zone Number ☐

Insights From Meditation

Date: ___/___/___

Daily Game Points

Core 4 Before the Door

Body: Did I Sweat Today? ☐ Yes ☐ No

    Fitness ☐ .5

    Fuel ☐ .5

Being:

    Meditation ☐ .5

    Memoirs ☐ .5

Balance:

    Partner ☐ .5

    Posterity ☐ .5

Business:

    Discovery ☐ .5

    Declare ☐ .5

Total / 4pts ☐

Power Zone ☐ 4 ☐ 3 ☐ 2 ☐ 1 ☐ DNC

Did I Stack? ☐ Yes 1pt ☐ No 0pts

Total Score (Core 4 + Stack pts) ☐

Power Zone Number ☐

Insights From Meditation

The General's Tent
Review & Report

Core 4 Points out of 28 ☐

Stack Points out of 7 ☐

Did I Complete the ONE THING? Yes = 1pt ☐

Did I Complete THE 4 KEYS? 1 point each + ☐

Total out of 40 ☐

Lessons Learned Within:

Body:

Being:

Balance:

Business:

The Stack:

The One Thing:

The Four Keys:

The General's Tent

Course Corrections?

Body:

Being:

Balance:

Business:

The Stack:

The One Thing:

The Four Keys:

Congratulations
Time to Celebrate!

A New Week

New Targets

Body:
Being:
Balance:
Business:

The ONE THING This Week

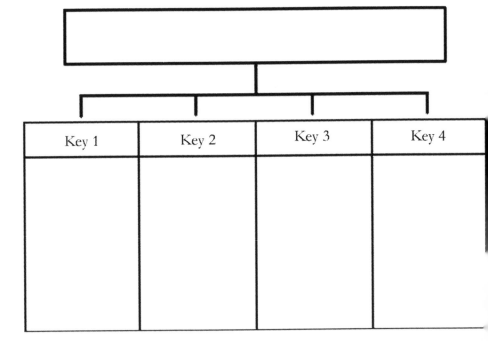

Key 1	Key 2	Key 3	Key 4

Key Actions

Key 1

What	
Why	
When	
How	

Key 2

What	
Why	
When	
How	

Key 3

What	
Why	
When	
How	

Key 4

What	
Why	
When	
How	

Date: ___/___/___

Daily Game Points

Core 4 Before the Door

Body: Did I Sweat Today?   ☐ Yes   ☐ No

    Fitness   ☐ .5

    Fuel   ☐ .5

Being:

    Meditation   ☐ .5

    Memoirs   ☐ .5

Balance:

    Partner   ☐ .5

    Posterity   ☐ .5

Business:

    Discovery   ☐ .5

    Declare   ☐ .5

Total / 4pts   ☐

Power Zone   ☐ 4   ☐ 3   ☐ 2   ☐ 1   ☐ DNC

Did I Stack?   ☐ Yes 1pt   ☐ No 0pts

Total Score (Core 4 + Stack pts)   ☐

Power Zone Number   ☐

Insights From Meditation

Date: ___/___/___

Daily Game Points

Core 4 Before the Door

Body: Did I Sweat Today? ☐ Yes   ☐ No
- Fitness ☐ .5
- Fuel ☐ .5

Being:
- Meditation ☐ .5
- Memoirs ☐ .5

Balance:
- Partner ☐ .5
- Posterity ☐ .5

Business:
- Discovery ☐ .5
- Declare ☐ .5

Total / 4pts ☐

Power Zone ☐ 4 ☐ 3 ☐ 2 ☐ 1 ☐ DNC

Did I Stack? ☐ Yes 1pt   ☐ No 0pts

Total Score (Core 4 + Stack pts) ☐

Power Zone Number ☐

Insights From Meditation

Date: ___/___/___

Daily Game Points

Core 4 Before the Door

Body: Did I Sweat Today? ☐ Yes ☐ No

    Fitness ☐ .5

    Fuel ☐ .5

Being:

    Meditation ☐ .5

    Memoirs ☐ .5

Balance:

    Partner ☐ .5

    Posterity ☐ .5

Business:

    Discovery ☐ .5

    Declare ☐ .5

Total / 4pts ☐

Power Zone ☐ 4 ☐ 3 ☐ 2 ☐ 1 ☐ DNC

Did I Stack? ☐ Yes 1pt ☐ No 0pts

Total Score (Core 4 + Stack pts) ☐

Power Zone Number ☐

Insights From Meditation

Date: __/__/__

Daily Game Points

Core 4 Before the Door

Body: Did I Sweat Today?   ☐ Yes   ☐ No

   Fitness   ☐ .5

   Fuel   ☐ .5

Being:

   Meditation   ☐ .5

   Memoirs   ☐ .5

Balance:

   Partner   ☐ .5

   Posterity   ☐ .5

Business:

   Discovery   ☐ .5

   Declare   ☐ .5

Total / 4pts   ☐

Power Zone   ☐ 4   ☐ 3   ☐ 2   ☐ 1   ☐ DNC

Did I Stack?   ☐ Yes 1pt   ☐ No 0pts

Total Score (Core 4 + Stack pts)   ☐

Power Zone Number   ☐

Insights From Meditation

Date: ___/___/___

Daily Game Points

Core 4 Before the Door

Body: Did I Sweat Today? ☐ Yes   ☐ No
- Fitness ☐ .5
- Fuel ☐ .5

Being:
- Meditation ☐ .5
- Memoirs ☐ .5

Balance:
- Partner ☐ .5
- Posterity ☐ .5

Business:
- Discovery ☐ .5
- Declare ☐ .5

Total / 4pts ☐

Power Zone ☐ 4   ☐ 3   ☐ 2   ☐ 1   ☐ DNC

Did I Stack? ☐ Yes 1pt   ☐ No 0pts

Total Score (Core 4 + Stack pts) ☐

Power Zone Number ☐

Insights From Meditation

Date: ___/___/_____

Daily Game Points

Core 4 Before the Door

Body: **Did I Sweat Today?** ☐ Yes   ☐ No

   Fitness ☐ .5

   Fuel ☐ .5

Being:

   Meditation ☐ .5

   Memoirs ☐ .5

Balance:

   Partner ☐ .5

   Posterity ☐ .5

Business:

   Discovery ☐ .5

   Declare ☐ .5

Total / 4pts ☐

Power Zone ☐ 4 ☐ 3 ☐ 2 ☐ 1 ☐ DNC

Did I Stack? ☐ Yes 1pt ☐ No 0pts

Total Score (Core 4 + Stack pts) ☐

Power Zone Number ☐

Insights From Meditation

Date: ___/___/___

Daily Game Points

Core 4 Before the Door

Body: **Did I Sweat Today?** ☐ Yes ☐ No

    Fitness ☐ .5

    Fuel ☐ .5

Being:

    Meditation ☐ .5

    Memoirs ☐ .5

Balance:

    Partner ☐ .5

    Posterity ☐ .5

Business:

    Discovery ☐ .5

    Declare ☐ .5

Total / 4pts ☐

Power Zone ☐ 4 ☐ 3 ☐ 2 ☐ 1 ☐ DNC

Did I Stack? ☐ Yes 1pt ☐ No 0pts

Total Score (Core 4 + Stack pts) ☐

Power Zone Number ☐

Insights From Meditation

The General's Tent
Review & Report

Core 4 Points out of 28 □

Stack Points out of 7 □

Did I Complete the ONE THING? Yes = 1pt □

Did I Complete THE 4 KEYS? 1 point each + □

Total out of 40 □

Lessons Learned Within:

Body:

Being:

Balance:

Business:

The Stack:

The One Thing:

The Four Keys:

The General's Tent

Course Corrections?

Body:

Being:

Balance:

Business:

The Stack:

The One Thing:

The Four Keys:

Congratulations
Time to Celebrate!

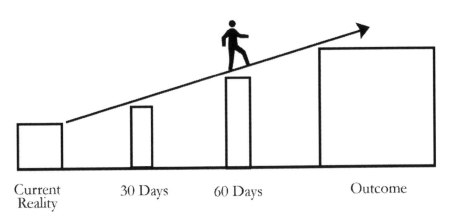

60 Day Benchmark

Current Reality — 30 Days — 60 Days — Outcome

Congratulations!

Where am I falling off?

Did I make the Outcome too small?

Benchmark Insights

A New Week

New Targets

Body:
Being:
Balance:
Business:

The ONE THING This Week

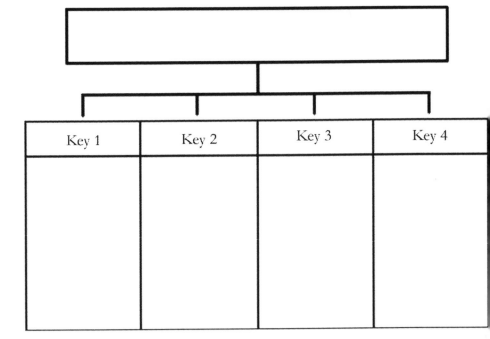

Key 1	Key 2	Key 3	Key 4

Key Actions

Key 1

What	
Why	
When	
How	

Key 2

What	
Why	
When	
How	

Key 3

What	
Why	
When	
How	

Key 4

What	
Why	
When	
How	

Date: __/__/__

Daily Game Points

Core 4 Before the Door

Body: Did I Sweat Today? ☐ Yes   ☐ No

   Fitness ☐ .5

   Fuel ☐ .5

Being:

   Meditation ☐ .5

   Memoirs ☐ .5

Balance:

   Partner ☐ .5

   Posterity ☐ .5

Business:

   Discovery ☐ .5

   Declare ☐ .5

Total / 4pts ☐

Power Zone ☐ 4 ☐ 3 ☐ 2 ☐ 1 ☐ DNC

Did I Stack? ☐ Yes 1pt   ☐ No 0pts

Total Score (Core 4 + Stack pts) ☐

Power Zone Number ☐

Insights From Meditation

Date: ___/___/___

Daily Game Points

Core 4 Before the Door

Body: Did I Sweat Today? ☐ Yes ☐ No

    Fitness ☐ .5

    Fuel ☐ .5

Being:

    Meditation ☐ .5

    Memoirs ☐ .5

Balance:

    Partner ☐ .5

    Posterity ☐ .5

Business:

    Discovery ☐ .5

    Declare ☐ .5

Total / 4pts ☐

Power Zone ☐ 4 ☐ 3 ☐ 2 ☐ 1 ☐ DNC

Did I Stack? ☐ Yes 1pt ☐ No 0pts

Total Score (Core 4 + Stack pts) ☐

Power Zone Number ☐

Insights From Meditation

Date: ___/___/___

Daily Game Points

Core 4 Before the Door

Body: Did I Sweat Today? ☐ Yes ☐ No

    Fitness   ☐ .5

    Fuel   ☐ .5

Being:

    Meditation   ☐ .5

    Memoirs   ☐ .5

Balance:

    Partner   ☐ .5

    Posterity   ☐ .5

Business:

    Discovery   ☐ .5

    Declare   ☐ .5

Total / 4pts   ☐

Power Zone   ☐ 4   ☐ 3   ☐ 2   ☐ 1   ☐ DNC

Did I Stack?   ☐ Yes 1pt   ☐ No 0pts

Total Score (Core 4 + Stack pts)   ☐

Power Zone Number   ☐

Insights From Meditation

Date: ___/___/___

Daily Game Points

Core 4 Before the Door

Body: Did I Sweat Today? ☐ Yes ☐ No

    Fitness ☐ .5

    Fuel ☐ .5

Being:

    Meditation ☐ .5

    Memoirs ☐ .5

Balance:

    Partner ☐ .5

    Posterity ☐ .5

Business:

    Discovery ☐ .5

    Declare ☐ .5

Total / 4pts ☐

Power Zone ☐ 4 ☐ 3 ☐ 2 ☐ 1 ☐ DNC

Did I Stack? ☐ Yes 1pt ☐ No 0pts

Total Score (Core 4 + Stack pts) ☐

Power Zone Number ☐

Insights From Meditation

Date: ___/___/___

Daily Game Points

Core 4 Before the Door

Body: **Did I Sweat Today?** ☐ Yes ☐ No

   Fitness ☐ .5

   Fuel ☐ .5

Being:

   Meditation ☐ .5

   Memoirs ☐ .5

Balance:

   Partner ☐ .5

   Posterity ☐ .5

Business:

   Discovery ☐ .5

   Declare ☐ .5

Total / 4pts ☐

Power Zone ☐ 4 ☐ 3 ☐ 2 ☐ 1 ☐ DNC

Did I Stack? ☐ Yes 1pt ☐ No 0pts

Total Score (Core 4 + Stack pts) ☐

Power Zone Number ☐

Insights From Meditation

Date: ___/___/___

Daily Game Points

Core 4 Before the Door

Body: Did I Sweat Today? ☐ Yes   ☐ No
- Fitness ☐ .5
- Fuel ☐ .5

Being:
- Meditation ☐ .5
- Memoirs ☐ .5

Balance:
- Partner ☐ .5
- Posterity ☐ .5

Business:
- Discovery ☐ .5
- Declare ☐ .5

Total / 4pts ☐

Power Zone ☐ 4   ☐ 3   ☐ 2   ☐ 1   ☐ DNC

Did I Stack? ☐ Yes 1pt   ☐ No 0pts

Total Score (Core 4 + Stack pts) ☐

Power Zone Number ☐

Insights From Meditation

Date: ___/___/___

Daily Game Points

Core 4 Before the Door

Body: Did I Sweat Today?   ☐ Yes   ☐ No

    Fitness   ☐ .5

    Fuel   ☐ .5

Being:

    Meditation ☐ .5

    Memoirs   ☐ .5

Balance:

    Partner   ☐ .5

    Posterity   ☐ .5

Business:

    Discovery   ☐ .5

    Declare   ☐ .5

Total / 4pts   ☐

Power Zone   ☐ 4   ☐ 3   ☐ 2   ☐ 1   ☐ DNC

Did I Stack?   ☐ Yes 1pt   ☐ No 0pts

Total Score (Core 4 + Stack pts)   ☐

Power Zone Number   ☐

Insights From Meditation

The General's Tent
Review & Report

Core 4 Points out of 28   ☐

Stack Points out of 7   ☐

Did I Complete the ONE THING? Yes = 1pt   ☐

Did I Complete THE 4 KEYS? 1 point each   **+** ☐

Total out of 40   ☐

Lessons Learned Within:

Body:

Being:

Balance:

Business:

The Stack:

The One Thing:

The Four Keys:

The General's Tent

Course Corrections?

Body:

Being:

Balance:

Business:

The Stack:

The One Thing:

The Four Keys:

Congratulations
Time to Celebrate!

A New Week

New Targets

Body:
Being:
Balance:
Business:

The ONE THING This Week

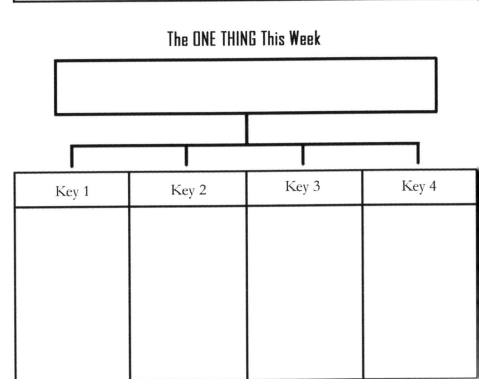

Key 1	Key 2	Key 3	Key 4

Key Actions

Key 1

What	
Why	
When	
How	

Key 2

What	
Why	
When	
How	

Key 3

What	
Why	
When	
How	

Key 4

What	
Why	
When	
How	

Date: ___ / ___ / ___

Daily Game Points

Core 4 Before the Door

Body: Did I Sweat Today? ☐ Yes   ☐ No

    Fitness ☐ .5

    Fuel ☐ .5

Being:

    Meditation ☐ .5

    Memoirs ☐ .5

Balance:

    Partner ☐ .5

    Posterity ☐ .5

Business:

    Discovery ☐ .5

    Declare ☐ .5

Total / 4pts ☐

Power Zone ☐ 4 ☐ 3 ☐ 2 ☐ 1 ☐ DNC

Did I Stack? ☐ Yes 1pt   ☐ No 0pts

Total Score (Core 4 + Stack pts) ☐

Power Zone Number ☐

Insights From Meditation

Date: ___/___/___

Daily Game Points

Core 4 Before the Door

Body: Did I Sweat Today?   ☐ Yes   ☐ No
    Fitness   ☐ .5
    Fuel   ☐ .5

Being:
    Meditation   ☐ .5
    Memoirs   ☐ .5

Balance:
    Partner   ☐ .5
    Posterity   ☐ .5

Business:
    Discovery   ☐ .5
    Declare   ☐ .5

Total / 4pts   ☐

Power Zone   ☐ 4   ☐ 3   ☐ 2   ☐ 1   ☐ DNC

Did I Stack?   ☐ Yes 1pt   ☐ No 0pts

Total Score (Core 4 + Stack pts)   ☐

Power Zone Number   ☐

Insights From Meditation

Date: ___/___/___

Daily Game Points

Core 4 Before the Door

Body: **Did I Sweat Today?** ☐ Yes ☐ No

    Fitness ☐ .5

    Fuel ☐ .5

Being:

    Meditation ☐ .5

    Memoirs ☐ .5

Balance:

    Partner ☐ .5

    Posterity ☐ .5

Business:

    Discovery ☐ .5

    Declare ☐ .5

Total / 4pts ☐

Power Zone ☐ 4 ☐ 3 ☐ 2 ☐ 1 ☐ DNC

Did I Stack? ☐ Yes 1pt ☐ No 0pts

Total Score (Core 4 + Stack pts) ☐

Power Zone Number ☐

Insights From Meditation

Date: ___/___/___

Daily Game Points

Core 4 Before the Door

Body: Did I Sweat Today? ☐ Yes ☐ No

- Fitness ☐ .5
- Fuel ☐ .5

Being:

- Meditation ☐ .5
- Memoirs ☐ .5

Balance:

- Partner ☐ .5
- Posterity ☐ .5

Business:

- Discovery ☐ .5
- Declare ☐ .5

Total / 4pts ☐

Power Zone ☐ 4 ☐ 3 ☐ 2 ☐ 1 ☐ DNC

Did I Stack? ☐ Yes 1pt ☐ No 0pts

Total Score (Core 4 + Stack pts) ☐

Power Zone Number ☐

Insights From Meditation

Date: ___/___/___

Daily Game Points

Core 4 Before the Door

Body: Did I Sweat Today? ☐ Yes ☐ No

    Fitness ☐ .5

    Fuel ☐ .5

Being:

    Meditation ☐ .5

    Memoirs ☐ .5

Balance:

    Partner ☐ .5

    Posterity ☐ .5

Business:

    Discovery ☐ .5

    Declare ☐ .5

Total / 4pts ☐

Power Zone ☐ 4 ☐ 3 ☐ 2 ☐ 1 ☐ DNC

Did I Stack? ☐ Yes 1pt ☐ No 0pts

Total Score (Core 4 + Stack pts) ☐

Power Zone Number ☐

Insights From Meditation

Date: ___/___/___

Daily Game Points

Core 4 Before the Door

Body: Did I Sweat Today? ☐ Yes ☐ No

    Fitness ☐ .5

    Fuel ☐ .5

Being:

    Meditation ☐ .5

    Memoirs ☐ .5

Balance:

    Partner ☐ .5

    Posterity ☐ .5

Business:

    Discovery ☐ .5

    Declare ☐ .5

Total / 4pts ☐

Power Zone ☐ 4 ☐ 3 ☐ 2 ☐ 1 ☐ DNC

Did I Stack? ☐ Yes 1pt ☐ No 0pts

Total Score (Core 4 + Stack pts) ☐

Power Zone Number ☐

Insights From Meditation

Date: ___/___/___

Daily Game Points

Core 4 Before the Door

Body: Did I Sweat Today? ☐ Yes   ☐ No

    Fitness ☐ .5

    Fuel ☐ .5

Being:

    Meditation ☐ .5

    Memoirs ☐ .5

Balance:

    Partner ☐ .5

    Posterity ☐ .5

Business:

    Discovery ☐ .5

    Declare ☐ .5

Total / 4pts ☐

Power Zone ☐ 4   ☐ 3   ☐ 2   ☐ 1   ☐ DNC

Did I Stack? ☐ Yes 1pt   ☐ No 0pts

Total Score (Core 4 + Stack pts) ☐

Power Zone Number ☐

Insights From Meditation

The General's Tent
Review & Report

Core 4 Points out of 28 ☐

Stack Points out of 7 ☐

Did I Complete the ONE THING? Yes = 1pt ☐

Did I Complete THE 4 KEYS? 1 point each **+** ☐

Total out of 40 ☐

Lessons Learned Within:

Body:

Being:

Balance:

Business:

The Stack:

The One Thing:

The Four Keys:

The General's Tent

Course Corrections?

Body:

Being:

Balance:

Business:

The Stack:

The One Thing:

The Four Keys:

Congratulations
Time to Celebrate!

A New Week

New Targets

Body:
Being:
Balance:
Business:

The ONE THING This Week

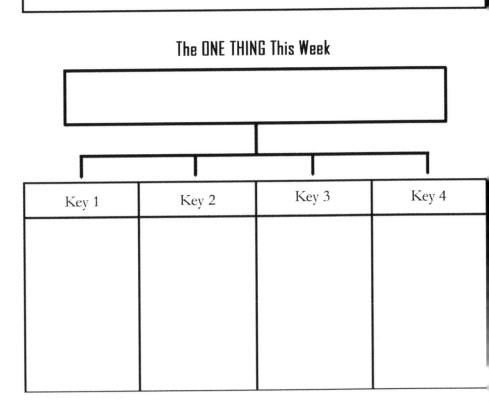

Key 1	Key 2	Key 3	Key 4

Key Actions

Key 1

What	
Why	
When	
How	

Key 2

What	
Why	
When	
How	

Key 3

What	
Why	
When	
How	

Key 4

What	
Why	
When	
How	

Date: ___ / ___ / ___

Daily Game Points

Core 4 Before the Door

Body: **Did I Sweat Today?** ☐ Yes ☐ No

    Fitness ☐ .5

    Fuel ☐ .5

Being:

    Meditation ☐ .5

    Memoirs ☐ .5

Balance:

    Partner ☐ .5

    Posterity ☐ .5

Business:

    Discovery ☐ .5

    Declare ☐ .5

Total / 4pts ☐

Power Zone ☐ 4 ☐ 3 ☐ 2 ☐ 1 ☐ DNC

Did I Stack? ☐ Yes 1pt ☐ No 0pts

Total Score (Core 4 + Stack pts) ☐

Power Zone Number ☐

Insights From Meditation

Date: ___/___/___

Daily Game Points

Core 4 Before the Door

Body: Did I Sweat Today? ☐ Yes ☐ No

    Fitness ☐ .5

    Fuel ☐ .5

Being:

    Meditation ☐ .5

    Memoirs ☐ .5

Balance:

    Partner ☐ .5

    Posterity ☐ .5

Business:

    Discovery ☐ .5

    Declare ☐ .5

Total / 4pts ☐

Power Zone ☐ 4 ☐ 3 ☐ 2 ☐ 1 ☐ DNC

Did I Stack? ☐ Yes 1pt ☐ No 0pts

Total Score (Core 4 + Stack pts) ☐

Power Zone Number ☐

Insights From Meditation

Date: ___ / ___ / ___

Daily Game Points

Core 4 Before the Door

Body: Did I Sweat Today? ☐ Yes   ☐ No

    Fitness ☐ .5

    Fuel ☐ .5

Being:

    Meditation ☐ .5

    Memoirs ☐ .5

Balance:

    Partner ☐ .5

    Posterity ☐ .5

Business:

    Discovery ☐ .5

    Declare ☐ .5

Total / 4pts ☐

Power Zone ☐ 4   ☐ 3   ☐ 2   ☐ 1   ☐ DNC

Did I Stack? ☐ Yes 1pt   ☐ No 0pts

Total Score (Core 4 + Stack pts) ☐

Power Zone Number ☐

Insights From Meditation

Date: ___/___/___

Daily Game Points

Core 4 Before the Door

Body: Did I Sweat Today?   ☐ Yes   ☐ No

    Fitness   ☐ .5

    Fuel   ☐ .5

Being:

    Meditation   ☐ .5

    Memoirs   ☐ .5

Balance:

    Partner   ☐ .5

    Posterity   ☐ .5

Business:

    Discovery   ☐ .5

    Declare   ☐ .5

Total / 4pts   ☐

Power Zone   ☐ 4   ☐ 3   ☐ 2   ☐ 1   ☐ DNC

Did I Stack?   ☐ Yes 1pt   ☐ No 0pts

Total Score (Core 4 + Stack pts)   ☐

Power Zone Number   ☐

Insights From Meditation

Date: __/ /__

Daily Game Points

Core 4 Before the Door

Body: Did I Sweat Today? ☐ Yes ☐ No
    Fitness ☐ .5
    Fuel ☐ .5

Being:
    Meditation ☐ .5
    Memoirs ☐ .5

Balance:
    Partner ☐ .5
    Posterity ☐ .5

Business:
    Discovery ☐ .5
    Declare ☐ .5

Total / 4pts ☐

Power Zone ☐ 4 ☐ 3 ☐ 2 ☐ 1 ☐ DNC

Did I Stack? ☐ Yes 1pt ☐ No 0pts

Total Score (Core 4 + Stack pts) ☐

Power Zone Number ☐

Insights From Meditation

Date: ___ / ___ / ___

Daily Game Points

Core 4 Before the Door

Body: Did I Sweat Today?   ☐ Yes   ☐ No

    Fitness   ☐ .5

    Fuel   ☐ .5

Being:

    Meditation   ☐ .5

    Memoirs   ☐ .5

Balance:

    Partner   ☐ .5

    Posterity   ☐ .5

Business:

    Discovery   ☐ .5

    Declare   ☐ .5

Total / 4pts   ☐

Power Zone   ☐ 4   ☐ 3   ☐ 2   ☐ 1   ☐ DNC

Did I Stack?   ☐ Yes 1pt   ☐ No 0pts

Total Score (Core 4 + Stack pts)   ☐

Power Zone Number   ☐

Insights From Meditation

Date: ___/___/___

Daily Game Points

Core 4 Before the Door

Body: Did I Sweat Today? ☐ Yes   ☐ No

    Fitness ☐ .5

    Fuel ☐ .5

Being:

    Meditation ☐ .5

    Memoirs ☐ .5

Balance:

    Partner ☐ .5

    Posterity ☐ .5

Business:

    Discovery ☐ .5

    Declare ☐ .5

Total / 4pts ☐

Power Zone ☐ 4   ☐ 3   ☐ 2   ☐ 1   ☐ DNC

Did I Stack? ☐ Yes 1pt   ☐ No 0pts

Total Score (Core 4 + Stack pts) ☐

Power Zone Number ☐

Insights From Meditation

The General's Tent
Review & Report

Core 4 Points out of 28   ☐

Stack Points out of 7   ☐

Did I Complete the ONE THING? Yes = 1pt   ☐

Did I Complete THE 4 KEYS? 1 point each   **+** ☐

Total out of 40   ☐

Lessons Learned Within:

Body:

Being:

Balance:

Business:

The Stack:

The One Thing:

The Four Keys:

The General's Tent

Course Corrections?

Body:	

Being:	

Balance:	

Business:	

The Stack:	

The One Thing:	

The Four Keys:	

Congratulations
Time to Celebrate!

A New Week

New Targets

Body:
Being:
Balance:
Business:

The ONE THING This Week

Key 1	Key 2	Key 3	Key 4

Key Actions

Key 1

What	
Why	
When	
How	

Key 2

What	
Why	
When	
How	

Key 3

What	
Why	
When	
How	

Key 4

What	
Why	
When	
How	

Date: ___/___/___

Daily Game Points

Core 4 Before the Door

Body: Did I Sweat Today? ☐ Yes ☐ No

    Fitness ☐ .5

    Fuel ☐ .5

Being:

    Meditation ☐ .5

    Memoirs ☐ .5

Balance:

    Partner ☐ .5

    Posterity ☐ .5

Business:

    Discovery ☐ .5

    Declare ☐ .5

Total / 4pts ☐

Power Zone ☐ 4 ☐ 3 ☐ 2 ☐ 1 ☐ DNC

Did I Stack? ☐ Yes 1pt ☐ No 0pts

Total Score (Core 4 + Stack pts) ☐

Power Zone Number ☐

Insights From Meditation

Date: ___/___/___

Daily Game Points

Core 4 Before the Door

Body: Did I Sweat Today? ☐ Yes   ☐ No
- Fitness ☐ .5
- Fuel ☐ .5

Being:
- Meditation ☐ .5
- Memoirs ☐ .5

Balance:
- Partner ☐ .5
- Posterity ☐ .5

Business:
- Discovery ☐ .5
- Declare ☐ .5

Total / 4pts ☐

Power Zone ☐ 4 ☐ 3 ☐ 2 ☐ 1 ☐ DNC

Did I Stack? ☐ Yes 1pt   ☐ No 0pts

Total Score (Core 4 + Stack pts) ☐

Power Zone Number ☐

Insights From Meditation

Date: ___/___/___

Daily Game Points

Core 4 Before the Door

Body: Did I Sweat Today? ☐ Yes   ☐ No

    Fitness   ☐ .5

    Fuel   ☐ .5

Being:

    Meditation   ☐ .5

    Memoirs   ☐ .5

Balance:

    Partner   ☐ .5

    Posterity   ☐ .5

Business:

    Discovery   ☐ .5

    Declare   ☐ .5

Total / 4pts   ☐

Power Zone   ☐ 4   ☐ 3   ☐ 2   ☐ 1   ☐ DNC

Did I Stack?   ☐ Yes 1pt   ☐ No 0pts

Total Score (Core 4 + Stack pts)   ☐

Power Zone Number   ☐

Insights From Meditation

Date: ___/___/___

Daily Game Points

Core 4 Before the Door

Body: Did I Sweat Today?   ☐ Yes   ☐ No

    Fitness   ☐ .5

    Fuel   ☐ .5

Being:

    Meditation   ☐ .5

    Memoirs   ☐ .5

Balance:

    Partner   ☐ .5

    Posterity   ☐ .5

Business:

    Discovery   ☐ .5

    Declare   ☐ .5

Total / 4pts   ☐

Power Zone   ☐ 4   ☐ 3   ☐ 2   ☐ 1   ☐ DNC

Did I Stack?   ☐ Yes 1pt   ☐ No 0pts

Total Score (Core 4 + Stack pts)   ☐

Power Zone Number   ☐

Insights From Meditation

Date: ___/___/___

Daily Game Points

Core 4 Before the Door

Body: Did I Sweat Today? ☐ Yes ☐ No

    Fitness ☐ .5

    Fuel ☐ .5

Being:

    Meditation ☐ .5

    Memoirs ☐ .5

Balance:

    Partner ☐ .5

    Posterity ☐ .5

Business:

    Discovery ☐ .5

    Declare ☐ .5

Total / 4pts ☐

Power Zone ☐ 4 ☐ 3 ☐ 2 ☐ 1 ☐ DNC

Did I Stack? ☐ Yes 1pt ☐ No 0pts

Total Score (Core 4 + Stack pts) ☐

Power Zone Number ☐

Insights From Meditation

Date: ___ / ___ / ___

Daily Game Points

Core 4 Before the Door

Body: **Did I Sweat Today?**   ☐ Yes   ☐ No

    Fitness   ☐ .5

    Fuel   ☐ .5

Being:

    Meditation   ☐ .5

    Memoirs   ☐ .5

Balance:

    Partner   ☐ .5

    Posterity   ☐ .5

Business:

    Discovery   ☐ .5

    Declare   ☐ .5

Total / 4pts   ☐

Power Zone   ☐ 4   ☐ 3   ☐ 2   ☐ 1   ☐ DNC

Did I Stack?   ☐ Yes 1pt   ☐ No 0pts

Total Score (Core 4 + Stack pts)   ☐

Power Zone Number   ☐

Insights From Meditation

Date: ___/___/___

Daily Game Points

Core 4 Before the Door

Body: Did I Sweat Today? ☐ Yes ☐ No

Fitness ☐ .5

Fuel ☐ .5

Being:

Meditation ☐ .5

Memoirs ☐ .5

Balance:

Partner ☐ .5

Posterity ☐ .5

Business:

Discovery ☐ .5

Declare ☐ .5

Total / 4pts ☐

Power Zone ☐ 4 ☐ 3 ☐ 2 ☐ 1 ☐ DNC

Did I Stack? ☐ Yes 1pt ☐ No 0pts

Total Score (Core 4 + Stack pts) ☐

Power Zone Number ☐

Insights From Meditation

The General's Tent
Review & Report

Core 4 Points out of 28 ☐

Stack Points out of 7 ☐

Did I Complete the ONE THING? Yes = 1pt ☐

Did I Complete THE 4 KEYS? 1 point each **+** ☐

Total out of 40 ☐

Lessons Learned Within:

Body:

Being:

Balance:

Business:

The Stack:

The One Thing:

The Four Keys:

The General's Tent

Course Corrections?

Body:

Being:

Balance:

Business:

The Stack:

The One Thing:

The Four Keys:

Congratulations
Time to Celebrate!

90 Day Outcome: Body

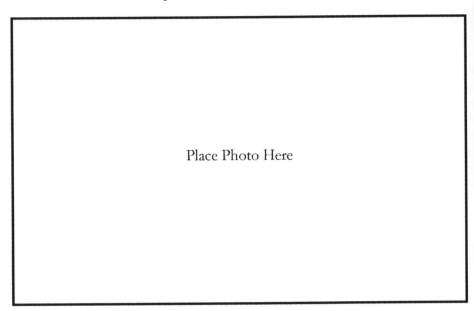

Place Photo Here

Celebrate!

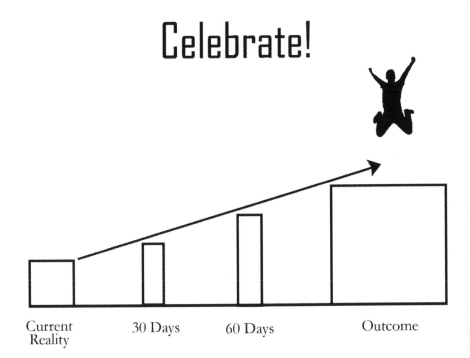

Current Reality   30 Days   60 Days   Outcome

90 Day Outcome Insights: Body

90 Day Outcome Insights: Being

90 Day Outcome Insights: Balance

90 Day Outcome Insights: Business

Made in the USA
Middletown, DE
22 January 2019